Scott Foresman - Addison Wesley

MATH

Review From Last Year Masters

Grade 5

Scott Foresman - Addison Wesley

Editorial Offices: Glenview, Illinois • New York, New York
Sales Offices: Reading, Massachusetts • Atlanta, Georgia • Glenview, Illinois
Carrollton, Texas • Menlo Park, California

http://www.sf.aw.com

Overview

Review From Last Year Masters provides a review of key concepts from the previous year of Scott Foresman - Addison Wesley MATH. Each of the 20 masters begins with an instructional model that is followed by practice.

Review From Last Year Masters can be used to determine how well students have retained concepts from the previous year and to prepare students for the upcoming year.

The *Answers and Options for Further Review* section at the back of this book provides alternatives for students who need additional reteaching and practice. Materials from the previous year (Student Edition lessons, Reteaching Masters, and Practice Masters) are keyed to each master.

ISBN 0-201-49633-X

Copyright © Addison Wesley Longman, Inc.

Printed in the United States of America

1 2 3 4 5 6 7 8 9 10 – CRK – 03 02 01 00 99 98

Contents

Interpreting Data

The **bar graph** shows the height of the World's Tallest Waterfalls. Lengths of bars represent heights of waterfalls.

What is the tallest waterfall?

Angel Falls is the tallest.

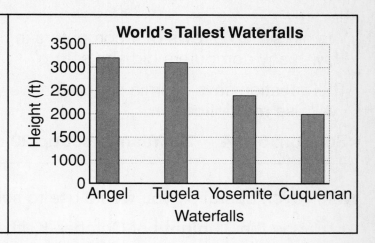

Use the graphs to answer each question.

1. What is the maximum life span of a jaguar? _____

2. Which animal has a life span of 13 years? _____

3. Draw the symbol for 10 years. _____

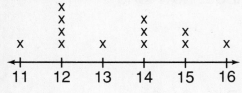

Maximum Life Span

○ = 4 years

Heights of Giraffes (nearest ft)

```
    x
    x            x
    x            x
    x    x   x   x   x
x   x    x   x   x   x
+--+----+---+---+---+---+
11  12   13  14  15  16
```

4. What is the most common giraffe height? _____

5. How many giraffes were 15-ft tall? _____

6. In which month were the most cars sold? _____

7. How many cars were sold in March? _____

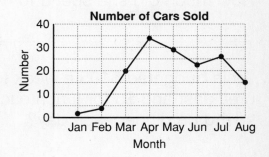

Problem Solving:
Analyze Word Problems

Yasmin set up 5 rows of 4 computers in the computer room. How many computers did she set up?

The question says Yasmin set up 5 rows with 4 computers in each row. I will use **multiplication.**

Solution: **5 × 4 = 20. Yasmin set up 20 computers.**

Write which operation you would use to solve each. Then solve.

1. During the **31 nights** of October, Keith kept track of his sleep. He slept a total of **279 hours.** How many hours of sleep did he **average** each night?

   _____ _____

2. The tallest building in Chicago, Sears Tower, is 1,454 ft tall. The tallest building in Dallas, Nations Bank Plaza, is 921 ft tall. How much taller than Nations Bank Plaza is Sears Tower?

   _____ _____

3. It takes the planet Mercury 88 days to orbit the sun. It takes Jupiter about 49 times that long. About how long does it take Jupiter to orbit the sun?

   _____ _____

4. Kirsten bought a TV set for $298 and a VCR for $149. How much did she spend for both items?

   _____ _____

5. Tania budgeted $105 a week for food. She plans $3 for breakfast and $5 for lunch each day. How much can she spend on dinner each day?

   _____ _____

Place Value Through Millions

Greater numbers can be written in three ways.

standard form	537,802,600
word form	**Five** hundred **thirty-seven** million, **eight** hundred **two** thousand, **six** hundred.
expanded form	500,000,000 + 30,000,000 + 7,000,000 + 800,000 + 2,000 + 600

Write the word name for each number.

1. 774,629,315 _____

_____

2. 415,394 _____

_____

Write the standard form for each number.

3. eighty-five million, three hundred forty-four thousand, twenty-nine

_____

4. ninety million, sixty-eight thousand, two hundred eighty _____

5. five hundred fifty-six thousand, eight hundred one _____

Write the expanded form of each number.

6. 37,960,044 _____

_____

7. eight million, one hundred fifty thousand, eleven

_____

Adding and Subtracting Whole Numbers

Find 354 + 581.

Add ones.	Add tens. Regroup.	Add hundreds.
3 7 **4** + 5 8 **1** **5**	**1** 3 7 4 + 5 8 1 **5** 5	**1** 3 7 4 + 5 8 1 **9** 5 5

Find 409 − 184.

Subtract ones.	Regroup. Subtract tens.	Subtract hundreds.
4 0 **9** − 1 8 **4** **5**	3 10 4 0̸ 9 − 1 8 4 **2** 5	3 10 4 0̸ 9 − 1 8 4 **2** 2 5

Find each sum or difference.

1.
  ¹
  6 **6**
+4 2 **9**
    5

2.
  6 12
6 7̸ **2**
− 2 5 **5**
    7

3.
7 0 9
+ 5 5 1

4.
8 4 9
− 4 7 0

5.
  6 1
+3 8 8

6.
7 8 9
+5 5 6

7.
$4 0 3
− 1 9 8

8.
9 7 0
− 2 5 5

9.
3 2 8
− 1 0 9

10.
8 7 0
− 4 4 4

11.
  3 2
4 0 6
+ 8 8 8

12.
9 0 0
8 4 4
+ 6 6

13. There are 415 students at Lincoln School this year. Last year there were 387 students. How many more students are there this year than last year?

_____

Multiplication and Division Facts

Ben bought tickets to the ice-skating rink for himself and his friends.
The total cost for 8 tickets was $32. How much did each ticket cost?

To solve, find 32 ÷ 8.　　**Think:** 8 times what number equals 32?

$$8 \times \mathbf{4} = 32$$

$$32 \div 8 = \mathbf{4}$$

Each ticket cost $4.

Find each product or quotient.

1. 49 ÷ 7 = ___　**2.** 6 × 4 = ___　**3.** 7 × 4 = ___　**4.** 63 ÷ 9 = ___

5. 9 ÷ 9 = ___　**6.** 42 ÷ 6 = ___　**7.** 6 × 8 = ___　**8.** 9 × 4 = ___

9. 9 × 7 = ___　**10.** 35 ÷ 7 = ___　**11.** 5 × 6 = ___　**12.** 32 ÷ 8 = ___

13.　　7
　　　　× 1
　　　　─────

14.　　6
　　　　× 8
　　　　─────

15.　　9
　　　　× 6
　　　　─────

16.　　0
　　　　× 8
　　　　─────

17. 6)5 4　　　**18.** 8)4 0　　　**19.** 9)4 5　　　**20.** 7)5 6

21. Marsha makes decorative candles. She packs the
candles 6 to a box. Last week she made 42 candles.
How many boxes will she need?　　

22. Shiji walks 5 miles each day. How many miles does
she walk each week?　　

23. Rose bought 3 books for $24. If each book was
the same price, how much did each book cost?　　_____

Multiplying by 1-Digit Factors

Find 4 × 168.

Multiply the ones. Regroup.	Multiply the tens. Add any extra tens. Regroup.	Multiply the hundreds. Add any extra hundreds.
$\begin{array}{r} 3 \\ 16\mathbf{8} \\ \times\quad 4 \\ \hline 2 \end{array}$	$\begin{array}{r} 2\,3 \\ 1\mathbf{6}8 \\ \times\quad 4 \\ \hline 7\,2 \end{array}$	$\begin{array}{r} 2\,3 \\ \mathbf{1}68 \\ \times\quad 4 \\ \hline 6\,7\,2 \end{array}$

Find each product.

1.
$$\begin{array}{r} {\scriptstyle 1} \\ 1\,2\,3 \\ \times\quad 6 \\ \hline 8 \end{array}$$

2.
$$\begin{array}{r} 2\,4\,4 \\ \times\quad 2 \\ \hline \end{array}$$

3.
$$\begin{array}{r} 1\,5\,3 \\ \times\quad 5 \\ \hline \end{array}$$

4.
$$\begin{array}{r} 3\,0\,0 \\ \times\quad 6 \\ \hline \end{array}$$

5.
$$\begin{array}{r} 6\,1\,3 \\ \times\quad 4 \\ \hline \end{array}$$

6.
$$\begin{array}{r} 5\,0\,2 \\ \times\quad 7 \\ \hline \end{array}$$

7.
$$\begin{array}{r} 3\,3\,6 \\ \times\quad 4 \\ \hline \end{array}$$

8.
$$\begin{array}{r} 7\,0\,9 \\ \times\quad 6 \\ \hline \end{array}$$

9.
$$\begin{array}{r} 8\,1\,1 \\ \times\quad 9 \\ \hline \end{array}$$

10.
$$\begin{array}{r} 4\,6\,0 \\ \times\quad 5 \\ \hline \end{array}$$

11.
$$\begin{array}{r} 6\,2\,2 \\ \times\quad 8 \\ \hline \end{array}$$

12.
$$\begin{array}{r} 2\,8\,9 \\ \times\quad 3 \\ \hline \end{array}$$

13.
$$\begin{array}{r} 4\,4\,4 \\ \times\quad 7 \\ \hline \end{array}$$

14.
$$\begin{array}{r} 8\,0\,2 \\ \times\quad 8 \\ \hline \end{array}$$

15.
$$\begin{array}{r} 3\,6\,7 \\ \times\quad 5 \\ \hline \end{array}$$

16.
$$\begin{array}{r} 9\,8\,7 \\ \times\quad 6 \\ \hline \end{array}$$

17. Mr. Reid bought 5 printers for the computer lab. Each printer cost $349. Find the total cost. _____

Multiplying by 2-Digit Factors

Find 63 × 74.

Multiply the ones. Regroup.	Multiply the tens. Regroup.	Add the partial products.
$\overset{1}{6}3$ × 7 **4** **2 5 2** ← 4 × 63	$\overset{2}{6}3$ × 7 **4** 2 5 2 **4 4 1 0** ← 70 × 63	6 3 × 7 4 **2 5 2** **4 4 1 0** **4 6 6 2** ← 252 + 4410

Find each product.

1. $\overset{1}{2}3$
    × 7 **5**
    1 1 5 ← 5 × 23
    + _____ ← 70 × 23

2. 3 8
    × 2 6
    _____ ← 6 × 38
    + _____ ← 20 × 38

3. 3 5
    × 1 6

4. 4 4
    × 3 0

5. 5 8
    × 1 8

6. 7 3
    × 2 7

7. 8 1
    × 1 9

8. 5 0
    × 4 1

9. 9 4
    × 6 3

10. 6 6
    × 2 9

11. A box contained 36 books. Each book sold for $29. Find the total value of the books.

_____

Dividing by 1-Digit Divisors

Find 238 ÷ 7.

Start the quotient in the tens place. (7 > 2)	Divide 7 into 23. Bring down remaining tens.	Bring down the ones. and divide 7 into 28.
7)2 3 8 ↑ ↑	3 7)2 3 8 2 1 2	3 4 7)2 3 8 2 1 2 8 2 8 0

Find each quotient.

1.
$$\begin{array}{r} 5 \\ 8)\overline{4\ 5\ 6} \end{array}$$
4 0

2. 6)3 4 8

3. 4)8 3 2

4. 5)3 6 0

5. 6)2 1 0

6. 7)3 3 6

7. 4)3 3 2

8. 4)1 2 8

9. 9)4 7 7

10. 8)4 4 8

11. 3)1 1 7

12. 6)4 0 2

13. The Soccer League has 448 players with 14 players on each team. How many teams are there? _____

Polygons

A polygon is a **closed shape** with **straight edges** only.

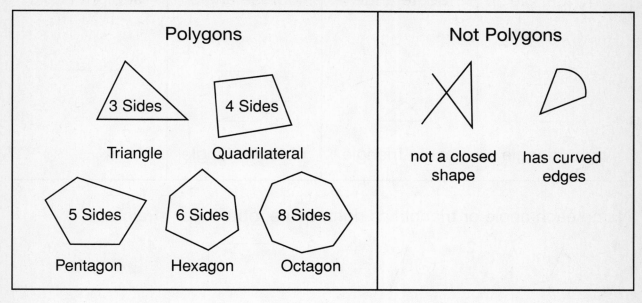

Polygons	Not Polygons
3 Sides — Triangle	not a closed shape
4 Sides — Quadrilateral	has curved edges
5 Sides — Pentagon	
6 Sides — Hexagon	
8 Sides — Octagon	

Tell if the figure is a polygon. If it is, tell what type of polygon it is.

1.

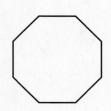

polygon

triangle

2.

_____

_____

3.

_____

_____

4.

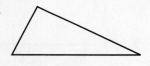

_____

_____

5.

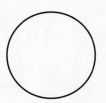

_____

_____

6.

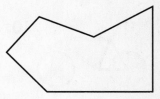

_____

_____

Triangles and Angles

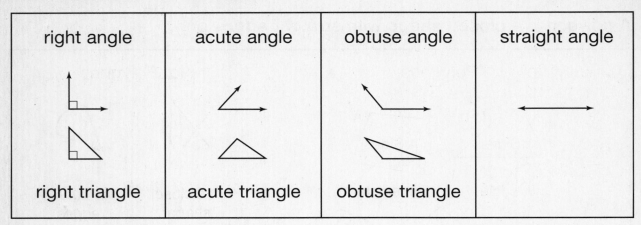

right angle	acute angle	obtuse angle	straight angle
right triangle	acute triangle	obtuse triangle	

Name each angle or triangle as right, acute, obtuse, or straight.

1.

2.

3.

4.

_____

5.

6.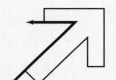

7.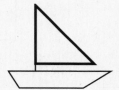

8.

Flag of Jamaica

_____

9.

10.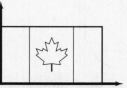

Flag of Canada

11.

12.

_____

Problem Solving: Analyze Strategies

Bess Fences made Ms. Wills a fence for her 5 foot by 7 foot garden. There was a 1 foot path between the fence and garden. What is the perimeter of the fence and the area it encloses?

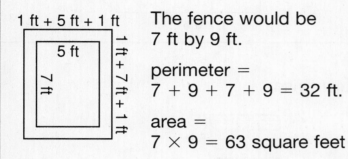

1 ft + 5 ft + 1 ft

5 ft

7 ft

1 ft + 7 ft + 1 ft

The fence would be 7 ft by 9 ft.

perimeter =
7 + 9 + 7 + 9 = 32 ft.

area =
7 × 9 = 63 square feet

**Problem Solving
Strategies**

- Use Objects/Act It Out
- **Draw a Picture**
- Look For a Pattern
- Guess and Check
- Make an Organized List
- Make a Table
- Solve a Simpler Problem
- Work Backward

Solve the following problems about Bess Fences. Use any strategy.

1. Mr. Fleming wanted a fence for his square patio. The area of the patio is 36 square feet. What would the perimeter of the fence be?

   perimeter = _____

2. Terri planned a fence for her pool. She asked Bess Fences to fence the largest area possible using 40 feet of fencing. What was the area?

   largest area = _____

3. Malcolm wanted to build a dog run with an area of 64 feet. What is the smallest perimeter the dog run could be?

   smallest perimeter = _____

4. Fencing costs $6 a foot. What would the least expensive fence for an area of 48 square feet cost? What would the most expensive fence for the same area cost? Each width and length must be a whole number.

   least expensive = _____   most expensive = _____

Volume

What is the volume of the rectangular prism?

Volume = length × width × height

= 6 × 2 × 3

= 36 cubic inches

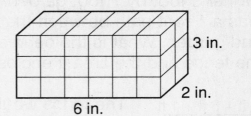

3 in.

2 in.

6 in.

Find the volume of each rectangular prism.

1.
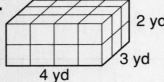
2 yd
3 yd
4 yd

4 × 3 × 2 = _____ cubic yards

2.
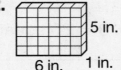
5 in.
6 in.   1 in.

_____

3.
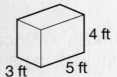
4 ft
3 ft   5 ft

_____

4.
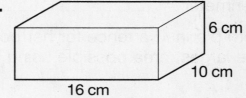
6 cm
10 cm
16 cm

_____

5.
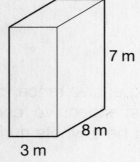
7 m
8 m
3 m

_____

6.
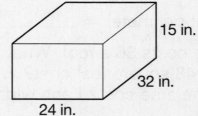
15 in.
32 in.
24 in.

_____

Name _____

Fractions

Write a fraction for the shaded part.

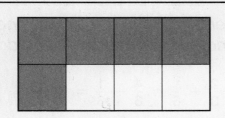

number of shaded squares → $\frac{5}{}$

number of squares → $\frac{}{8}$

The fraction is $\frac{5}{8}$.

Write a fraction for each shaded part.

1.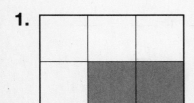

number of shaded squares →

number of squares →

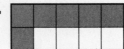

The fraction is _____.

2. 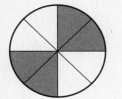 _____

3. 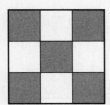 _____

4.   _____

5. _____

6. 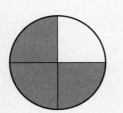 _____

7. 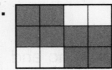 _____

Adding Fractions

Add $\frac{2}{9} + \frac{5}{9}$.

Add $\frac{2}{3} + \frac{1}{6}$.

If the denominators are the same, just add the numerators.	If the denominators are unlike, find a common denominator. Then add.
$$\frac{2}{9} + \frac{5}{9} = \frac{7}{9}$$	$$\frac{2}{3} + \frac{1}{6} = \frac{4}{6} + \frac{1}{6} = \frac{5}{6}$$

Find the sum. Simplify your answer if necessary.

1. $\frac{3}{8} + \frac{1}{4} = \frac{}{8} + \frac{}{8} = $ ——

2. $\frac{1}{2} + \frac{1}{3} = $ —— $+$ —— $=$ ——

3. $\frac{4}{9} + \frac{3}{9} = $ _____

4. $\frac{7}{12} + \frac{2}{12} = $ _____

5. $\frac{3}{10} + \frac{3}{10} = $ _____

6. $\frac{1}{6} + \frac{1}{6} = $ _____

7. $\frac{2}{5} + \frac{1}{10} = $ _____

8. $\frac{1}{3} + \frac{1}{6} = $ _____

9. $\frac{5}{12} + \frac{1}{4} = $ _____

10. $\frac{1}{4} + \frac{3}{5} = $ _____

11. $\frac{1}{3} + \frac{5}{9} = $ _____

12. Meg spent $\frac{3}{8}$ hour reading and $\frac{1}{2}$ hour doing homework. What fraction of an hour did she spend reading and doing homework?

_____

Subtracting Fractions

Subtract $\frac{7}{10} - \frac{6}{10}$.   Subtract $\frac{7}{8} - \frac{1}{2}$.

If the denominators are the same, just subtract the numerators.	If the denominators are unlike, find a common denominator. Then subtract.
$\frac{7}{10} - \frac{6}{10} = \frac{1}{10}$	$\frac{7}{8} - \frac{1}{2} = \frac{7}{8} - \frac{4}{8} = \frac{3}{8}$

Find the difference. Simplify your answer if necessary.

1. $\frac{7}{8} - \frac{1}{4} = \frac{}{8} - \frac{}{8} = $ —   **2.** $\frac{5}{6} - \frac{1}{5} = $ —— $-$ —— $ = $ ——

3. $\frac{7}{8} - \frac{2}{8} = $ _____   **4.** $\frac{4}{6} - \frac{1}{6} = $ _____   **5.** $\frac{3}{4} - \frac{1}{4} = $ _____

6. $\frac{8}{11} - \frac{5}{11} = $ _____   **7.** $\frac{4}{5} - \frac{1}{10} = $ _____   **8.** $\frac{7}{9} - \frac{1}{3} = $ _____

9. $\frac{3}{4} - \frac{5}{8} = $ _____   **10.** $\frac{11}{12} - \frac{1}{6} = $ _____   **11.** $\frac{7}{15} - \frac{2}{5} = $ _____

12. A recipe calls for $\frac{7}{8}$ cup of flour, but Paul has only $\frac{1}{2}$ cup. How much more flour does he need? _____

Measurement

Customary Units of Measure	Metric Units of Measure

Customary Units of Measure

Length
1 foot (ft)   = 12 inches (in.)
1 yard (yd) = 36 in.
                  = 3 ft
1 mile (mi) = 5,280 ft
                  = 1,760 yd

Weight
1 pound (lb) = 16 ounces (oz)
1 ton (T)   = 2,000 lb

Metric Units of Measure

Length
1 centimeter (cm) = 10 millimeters (mm)
1 decimeter (dm) = 100 mm
                           = 10 cm
1 meter (m)   = 1,000 mm
                           = 100 cm
                           = 10 dm
1 kilometer (km)   = 1,000 m

Mass
1 gram (g)   = 1,000 milligrams (mg)
1 kilogram (kg)   = 1,000 g
1 metric ton (t)   = 1,000 kg

Complete: 9 ft = ___?___ yd

A yard is **bigger** than a foot.

I should **divide: 9 ÷ 3 = 3.**

| | 1 yard |
| | 3 feet |

So, 9 ft = 3 yd.

1. 6 ft = ___?___ in.

An inch is _____ than a foot.

I should _____ : _____ .

| | 12 inches |
| | 1 foot |

So, 6 ft = _____ in.

Complete.

2. 6 ft = _____ yd   **3.** 48 oz = _____ lb   **4.** 2,000 m = _____ km

5. 5 gm = _____ mg   **6.** 3 mi = _____ ft   **7.** 72 in. = _____ yd

8. 1,000 lb = _____ T   **9.** 7 m = _____ cm   **10.** 6 in. = _____ ft

11. 10 lb = _____ oz   **12.** 880 yd = _____ mi   **13.** 6,000 mm = _____ m

14. A circus elephant weighed 6 tons.
How many pounds did it weigh?   _____

Name _____

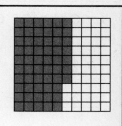

Decimals

Write the fraction, decimal, and word name for each shaded part.

3 out of 10 = $\frac{3}{10}$

     = 0.3

     = three-tenths

57 out of 100 = $\frac{57}{100}$

     = 0.57

     = fifty-seven hundredths

Write the fraction, decimal, and word name for each shaded part.

1.

$\square$ out of $\square$ = $\frac{\square}{\square}$

= _____

= _____

2.

$\square$ out of $\square$ = $\frac{\square}{\square}$

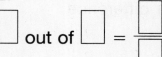 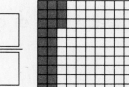

= _____

= _____

3.

_____

_____

_____

4.

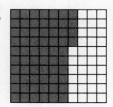

_____

_____

_____

Write the decimal for each.

5. $\frac{1}{10}$ _____

6. $\frac{52}{100}$ _____

7. $\frac{95}{100}$ _____

8. $\frac{8}{10}$ _____

9. $\frac{60}{100}$ _____

10. $\frac{3}{100}$ _____

11. sixteen hundredths _____

12. two tenths _____

13. A storm dropped eighty-eight hundredths of an inch of rain on Zenith Heights. Write the amount of rain as a fraction and as a decimal. _____ _____

Adding and Subtracting Decimals

Find 4.8 + 3.29.   Find 24.39 − 2.8.

Line up the decimal points.	Line up the decimal points.
↓	↓
4.8 4.8 **0** ← Write zeros	**3 13**
+ 3.2 9 + 3.2 9 as needed	2 4.3 9 2 4.3̸9̸ Write zeros
8.0 9	− 2.8 − 2.8 **0** ← as needed
↑ Place decimal	2 1.5 9
point in answer.	↑ Place decimal
	point in answer.

Find each sum or difference.

↓   ↓

1.   7.8 9   **2.**   6 2.7 **0**   **3.**   1 1 7   **4.**   2 4
   + 3 8.5 **0**   −   7.4 5   +   8 8.5   −   8.2
          .   .

5.   3.7 8   **6.**   3 0   **7.**   4 5.9   **8.**   7.7
   + 1 1 9.5   −   0.8   + 8 8.6 6   − 5.5 5

9. 41 − 3.2 = _____   **10.** 16.8 − 7.91 = _____

11. 58 + 6.7 + 100.33 = _____   **12.** 0.68 + 200 + 4.5 = _____

13. Three Shuttle missions lasted 11 days, 7.4 days, and 9.75 days, respectively. Find the total length of the three missions.   _____

Dividing by 2-Digit Divisors

Find 644 ÷ 28.

Start the quotient in the tens place. (28 < 64)	Divide 28 into 64. Bring down remaining tens.	Bring down the ones and divide 28 into 64.
28)6 4 4 ↑ ↑	$\begin{array}{r} 2 \\ 28\overline{)6\ 4\ 4} \\ 5\ 6 \\ \hline 8 \end{array}$	$\begin{array}{r} 2\ 3 \\ 28\overline{)6\ 4\ 4} \\ 5\ 6 \\ \hline 8\ 4 \\ 8\ 4 \\ \hline 0 \end{array}$

Find each quotient.

1. $\begin{array}{r} 2 \\ 11\overline{)2\ 4\ 2} \\ 2\ 2 \end{array}$

2. 28)3 3 6

3. 19)5 8 9

4. 812 ÷ 29 = _____

5. 666 ÷ 18 = _____

6. 945 ÷ 45 = _____

7. 832 ÷ 52 = _____

8. 984 ÷ 41 = _____

9. 938 ÷ 14 = _____

10. A shipment of 24 bicycles weighed 1,056 lb. If all the bicycles are the same, how much did each one weigh? _____

Probability

What is the probability of spinning a B?

$\dfrac{3}{8}$ ← number of Bs
← number of sections

The probability of spinning a B is $\dfrac{3}{8}$.

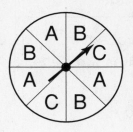

Complete.

1. What is the probability of spinning
a C on the above spinner? _____

number of Cs → ⬜
number of sections → ⬜

Use the spinners for 2–4 and 5–7. Write the probability of each event.

2. spinning a 5 _____

3. spinning an odd number _____

4. spinning a number greater than 2 _____

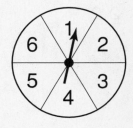

5. spinning dog or cat _____

6. spinning duck _____

7. spinning goat, cat, dog, or sheep _____

8. A number cube has six sides numbered 1 to 6.
What is the probability that you will roll 1 or 2? _____

9. A hat contains 40 cards each printed with a different
number from 1 to 40. What is the probability that
you will pick a number that has a zero in it? _____

Answers

REVIEW 1

If students need more help on interpreting data, use Lessons 1-1 through 1-5 from the 4th-grade book, along with the corresponding Practice and Reteaching Masters.

1. 23 years
2. salmon
3. ○ ○ ▽
4. 12 ft
5. 2 giraffes
6. April
7. 20

REVIEW 2

If students need more help on problem solving, use Lesson 1-7 from the 4th-grade book, along with the corresponding Practice and Reteaching Masters.

1. division; 9 hours
2. subtraction; 533 ft
3. multiplication; about 4,312 days
4. addition; $447
5. all operations; $7

REVIEW 3

If students need more help on place value through millions, use Lesson 2-3 from the 4th-grade book, along with the corresponding Practice and Reteaching Masters.

1. seven hundred seventy-four million, six hundred twenty-nine thousand, three hundred fifteen
2. four hundred fifteen thousand, three hundred ninety-four
3. 85,344,029
4. 90,068,280
5. 556,801
6. 30,000,000 + 7,000,000 + 900,000 + 60,000 + 40 + 4
7. 8,000,000 + 100,000 + 50,000 + 10 + 1

REVIEW 4

If students need more help on adding and subtracting whole numbers, use Lessons 3-5 through 3-8 from the 4th-grade book, along with the corresponding Practice and Reteaching Masters.

1. 495	2. 417	3. 1,260
4. 379	5. 449	6. 1,345
7. 205	8. 715	9. 219
10. 426	11. 1,326	12. 1,810
13. 28 students		

REVIEW 5

If students need more help on multiplication and division facts, use Chapter 4 from the 4th-grade book, along with the corresponding Practice and Reteaching Masters.

1. 7	2. 24	3. 28	4. 7
5. 1	6. 7	7. 48	8. 36
9. 63	10. 5	11. 30	12. 4
13. 7	14. 48	15. 54	16. 0
17. 9	18. 5	19. 5	20. 8
21. 7 boxes		22. 35 miles	
23. $8			

REVIEW 6

If students need more help on multiplying by 1-digit factors, use Chapter 5 from the 4th-grade book, along with the corresponding Practice and Reteaching Masters.

1. 738	2. 488	3. 765
4. 1,800	5. 2,452	6. 3,514
7. 1,344	8. 4,254	9. 7,299
10. 2,300	11. 4,976	12. 867
13. 3,108	14. 6,416	15. 1,835
16. 5,922	17. $1,745	

REVIEW 7

If students need more help on multiplying by 2-digit factors, use Chapter 6 from the 4th-grade book, along with the corresponding Practice and Reteaching Masters.

1. 1,725   **2.** 988
3. 560   **4.** 1,320   **5.** 1,044
6. 1,971   **7.** 1,539   **8.** 2,050
9. 5,922   **10.** 1,914   **11.** $1,044

REVIEW 8

If students need more help on dividing by 1-digit divisors, use Chapter 7 from the 4th-grade book, along with the corresponding Practice and Reteaching Masters.

1. 57   **2.** 58   **3.** 208   **4.** 72
5. 35   **6.** 48   **7.** 83   **8.** 32
9. 53   **10.** 56   **11.** 39   **12.** 67
13. 32 teams

REVIEW 9

If students need more help on polygons, use Lesson 8-2 from the 4th-grade book, along with the corresponding Practice and Reteaching Masters.

1. polygon; triangle
2. polygon; pentagon
3. not a polygon
4. polygon; octagon
5. not a polygon
6. polygon; hexagon

REVIEW 10

If students need more help on triangles and angles, use Lesson 8-4 from the 4th-grade book, along with the corresponding Practice and Reteaching Masters.

1. obtuse   **2.** straight   **3.** right
4. acute   **5.** obtuse   **6.** acute
7. right   **8.** straight   **9.** acute
10. right   **11.** acute   **12.** straight

REVIEW 11

If students need more help on the strategy Draw a Picture, use Lesson 6-11 from the 4th-grade book, along with the corresponding Practice and Reteaching Masters.

1. 24 feet   **2.** 100 square feet
3. 32 feet
4. least expensive: $168
most expensive: $588

REVIEW 12

If students need more help on volume, use Lesson 8-13 from the 4th-grade book, along with the corresponding Practice and Reteaching Masters.

1. 24 yd^3 **2.** 30 in^3
3. 60 ft^3 **4.** 960 cm^3
5. 168 m^3 **6.** 11,520 in^3

REVIEW 13

If students need more help on fractions, use Lesson 9-2 from the 4th-grade book, along with the corresponding Practice and Reteaching Masters.

1. $\frac{2}{6}$ **2.** $\frac{4}{8}$ **3.** $\frac{6}{10}$ **4.** $\frac{5}{9}$
5. $\frac{3}{6}$ **6.** $\frac{3}{4}$ **7.** $\frac{8}{12}$

REVIEW 14

If students need more help on adding fractions, use Lessons 10-1 through 10-3 from the 4th-grade book, along with the corresponding Practice and Reteaching Masters.

1. $\frac{5}{8}$ **2.** $\frac{5}{6}$ **3.** $\frac{7}{9}$
4. $\frac{9}{12} = \frac{3}{4}$ **5.** $\frac{6}{10} = \frac{3}{5}$ **6.** $\frac{2}{6} = \frac{1}{3}$
7. $\frac{5}{10} = \frac{1}{2}$ **8.** $\frac{3}{6} = \frac{1}{2}$ **9.** $\frac{8}{12} = \frac{2}{3}$
10. $\frac{17}{20}$ **11.** $\frac{8}{9}$ **12.** $\frac{7}{8}$ hour

REVIEW 15

If students need more help on subtracting fractions, use Lesson 10-6 from the 4th-grade book, along with the corresponding Practice and Reteaching Masters.

1. $\frac{5}{8}$ 2. $\frac{19}{30}$ 3. $\frac{5}{8}$

4. $\frac{3}{6} = \frac{1}{2}$ 5. $\frac{2}{4} = \frac{1}{2}$ 6. $\frac{3}{11}$

7. $\frac{7}{10}$ 8. $\frac{4}{9}$ 9. $\frac{1}{8}$

10. $\frac{9}{12} = \frac{3}{4}$ 11. $\frac{1}{15}$ 12. $\frac{3}{8}$ cup

REVIEW 16

If students need more help on measurement, use Lessons 9-11, 9-13, 10-8, 10-9, 11-10, 11-13, and 11-14 from the 4th-grade book, along with the corresponding Practice and Reteaching Masters.

1. 72 in.   2. 2 yd   3. 3 lb
4. 2 km   5. 5,000 mg   6. 15,840 ft

7. 2 yd   8. $\frac{1}{2}$ T   9. 700 cm

10. $\frac{1}{2}$ ft   11. 160 oz   12. $\frac{1}{2}$ mi

13. 6 m   14. 12,000 lb

REVIEW 17

If students need more help on decimals, use Lessons 11-1 through 11-6 from the 4th-grade book, along with the corresponding Practice and Reteaching Masters.

1. $\frac{7}{10}$, 0.7, seven-tenths

2. $\frac{23}{100}$, 0.23, twenty-three hundredths

3. $\frac{4}{10}$, 0.4, four-tenths

4. $\frac{64}{100}$, 0.64, sixty-four hundredths

5. 0.1   6. 0.52   7. 0.95   8. 0.8

9. 0.60   10. 0.03   11. 0.16   12. 0.2

13. $\frac{88}{100}$, 0.88

REVIEW 18

If students need more help on adding and subtracting decimals, use Lesson 11.9 from the 4th-grade book, along with the corresponding Practice and Reteaching Masters.

1. 46.39   2. 55.25   3. 205.5   4. 15.8
5. 123.28   6. 29.2   7. 134.56   8. 2.15
9. 37.8   10. 8.89
11. 165.03   12. 205.18
13. 28.15 days

REVIEW 19

If students need more help on dividing by 2-digit divisors, use Lesson 12-4 from the 4th-grade book, along with the corresponding Practice and Reteaching Masters.

1. 22   2. 12   3. 31   4. 28
5. 37   6. 21   7. 16   8. 24
9. 67   10. 44 lb

REVIEW 20

If students need more help on probability, use Lesson 12-9 from the 4th-grade book, along with the corresponding Practice and Reteaching Masters.

1. $\frac{2}{8} = \frac{1}{4}$ 2. $\frac{1}{6}$ 3. $\frac{1}{2}$

4. $\frac{2}{3}$ 5. $\frac{1}{2}$ 6. 0

7. 1   8. $\frac{1}{3}$ 9. $\frac{1}{10}$